Dino-snore

By Jenny Jinks

Illustrated by
Santhya Shenbagam
Radhakrishnan

Star loved to sleep.

She dozed all day...

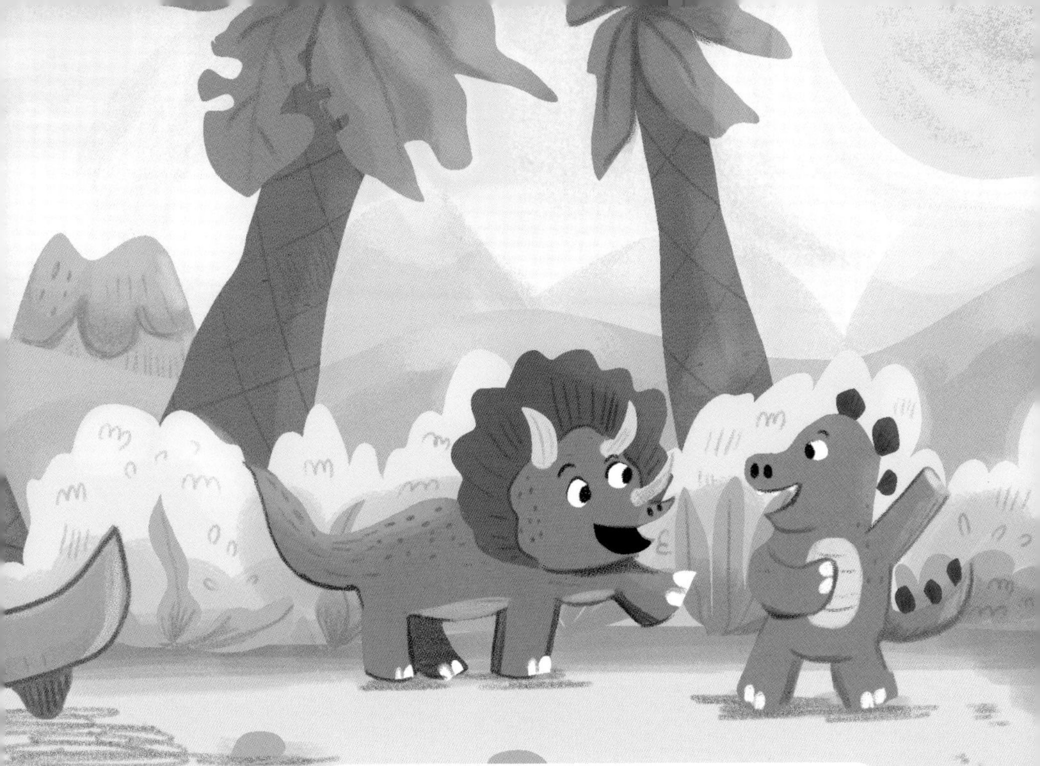

...and napped all night.

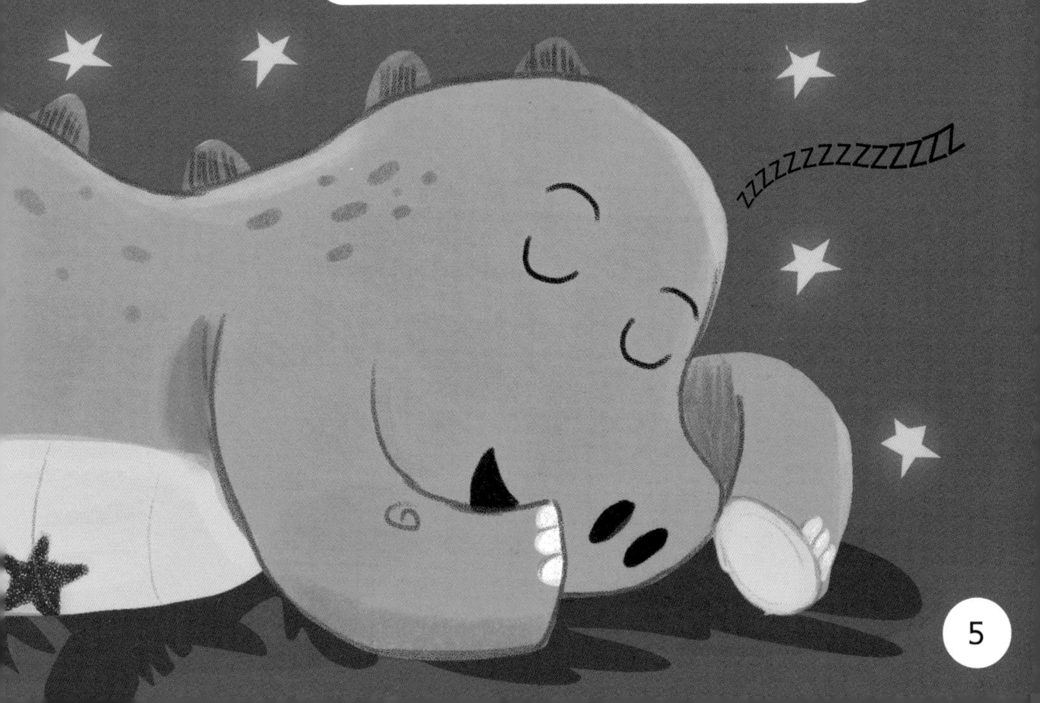
zzzzzzzzzzzzzzz

But the more Star slept, the less sleep

everyone else got.

Star's snore was a big problem.

"What can we do about Star?"

They were at a jungle meeting.

Star was snoozing at the back.

"I have an idea," said Fizz.

But just then, Kal burst in. "It's Spike!"

Spike was the biggest, scariest

beast in the whole jungle.

"He is on a rampage. And he is coming this way," said Kal. "Everyone hide!"

But it was too late.

"ROOOAAAAR!" roared Spike.

STOMP! STOMP! STOMP!

He crashed through the jungle, crushing

everything in his path.

"We must leave!" said Kal.

"But what about Star?" squeaked Fizz.

She was still fast asleep.

"No time. Run!" said Kal.

But Fizz could not just leave Star.

Then he had an idea.

Fizz marched right up to Spike. "HEY!"

Spike stopped. Nobody ever dared to speak to him.

"Don't go this way,"

Fizz said.

"Why not?"

said Spike.

"Because my friend will get you," said Fizz. "She's even bigger and scarier than you."

"Nobody is scarier than me," laughed Spike.

Then they heard a loud rumbling sound.

"ZZZZZZZZ... RAA RAARAA."

"What was that?" Spike asked.

"My friend," smiled Fizz.

"I'm not frightened," said Spike.

But he didn't look sure.

zzzzzzzzzzzzz

The rumbling came again, this time even louder. It made the ground quake. It made the trees shiver.

It made Spike shake with fear.

"You'd better run, or she'll find you,"
said Fizz.

Spike turned and ran, and he never came back.

"The jungle is safe," everyone cried.

"Hooray for Fizz."

"And Star!" Fizz said.

Star snored so loudly she woke herself up.

"Did I miss something?" she asked.

Everyone laughed.

Quiz

1. What does Star love to do?

a) Run

b) Sleep

c) Eat

2. What is a big problem?

a) Star's snore

b) Star's laugh

c) Star's smell

3. Who is the biggest, scariest beast in the whole jungle?

a) Star

b) Fizz

c) Spike

4. Who does not leave Star?

a) Spike

b) Fizz

c) Kal

5. Why does Star wake herself up at the end?

a) She snores loudly

b) She sneezes

c) She is hungry

Book Bands for Guided Reading

The Institute of Education book banding system is a scale of colours that reflects the various levels of reading difficulty. The bands are assigned by taking into account the content, the language style, the layout and phonics. Word, phrase and sentence level work is also taken into consideration.

Maverick Early Readers are a bright, attractive range of books covering the pink to white bands. All of these books have been book banded for guided reading to the industry standard and edited by a leading educational consultant.

To view the whole Maverick Readers scheme, visit our website at www.maverickearlyreaders.com

Or scan the QR code above to view our scheme instantly!

Quiz Answers: 1b, 2a, 3c, 4b, 5a